The South West

Edited By Daisy Job

First published in Great Britain in 2019 by:

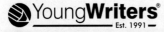 Young**Writers**®
Est. 1991

Young Writers
Remus House
Coltsfoot Drive
Peterborough
PE2 9BF
Telephone: 01733 890066
Website: www.youngwriters.co.uk

Foreword

Dear Reader,

You will never guess what I did today! Shall I tell you? Some primary school pupils wrote some diary entries and I got to read them, and they were **excellent!**

They wrote them in school and sent them to us here at Young Writers. We'd given their teachers some bright and funky worksheets to fill in, and some fun and fabulous (and free) resources to help spark ideas and get inspiration flowing.

And it clearly worked because **WOW!!** I can't believe the adventures I've been reading about. Real people, make believe people, dogs and unicorns, even objects like pencils all feature and these diaries all have one thing in common – they are **jam-packed** with imagination!

We live and breathe creativity here at Young Writers – it gives us life! We want to pass our love of the written word onto the next generation and what better way to do that than to celebrate their writing by publishing it in a book!

It sets their work free from homework books and notepads and puts it where it deserves to be – **out in the world!** Each awesome author in this book should be **super proud** of themselves, and now they've got proof of their imagination, their ideas and their creativity in black and white, to look back on in years to come!

Now that I've read all these diaries, I've somehow got to pick some winners! Oh my gosh it's going to be difficult to choose, but I'm going to have **so much fun** doing it!

Bye!

Daisy

Contents

Charlie Joce (7)   62
Sivatia Goligher (6)   63

St Joseph's RC Primary School, Highweek

Eliana Quainoo (7)   64
Isla McKinley (6)   66
Amelia Grant (7)   68
Evangeline Joy Peacock (6)   69
Annie Merrin Madeline Turner (7)   70
Brendon Letchford (7)   71
Isla Rose Hoskin (6)   72
Heidi Long (7)   73
Jessica-Jane Kneeshaw (7)   74
Harry James Robinson (6)   75
Filip Jaglowski (7)   76
Charlie Edge (7)   77
Bobbie-Rae Rawlings (7)   78
Ellis Gillam (6)   79
Robin Jack Harris (7)   80
Michael Hooper (7)   81
Grace Stoyle (6)   82

St Mark's VA Primary School, Worle

Sophia Peddle (7)   83
Bobbi Morley (7)   84
Oliver Rogers (7)   86
Ezmee Bobbin (7)   88
Emily Wellsbury (7)   90
Woody Milton (7)   92
Dexter Cunningham (7)   94
Annabelle Tonkinson (7)   96
Reegan Parkes (7)   98
Isobel Owen (7)   100
Lorelai Jimmieson (6)   102
Payton Lillie Stacey (7)   104
Erin Robinson (7)   106
Leah Gordon (7)   108
Stephen Vowles (7)   109
Charlie Mortimer (7)   110

Max Fitzgibbon (6)   111
Lauren Barlow (7)   112
Freddie Colman (7)   113
Olivia Knott (7)   114
Jacob Mikulla (7)   115
Lola Jessie Dyer (7)   116
Jaiden Moore (7)   117
Jessica Ambrose (7)   118
May Bailey (7)   119
Jessica Cunningham (7)   120
Bella Elizabeth Cawley (7)   121
Carly McDermott (7)   122
Connie Harvey-Comer (7)   123
Layla Enver (7)   124
Ellis D'Arcy   125
Leon Neate (6)   126
Lillie-Rose Biss (7)   127
James Morrissey (7)   128
Rosie Seckham (7)   129
Logan Hughes (7)   130
Harry Hucker (7)   131
Ashton Robinson (7)   132
Darci Garside (7)   133
Oliver James Walton (7)   134
Ciaran Rees (7)   135
Jax Ager (6)   136
Harrison Roberts (7)   137
Rory Bishop (7)   138

Sunninghill Preparatory School, South Walks

Scarlett (7)   139
Tabitha Margarette May Buchan-Moore (7)   140
Leo Hemingway (7)   142
Natty Savva (7)   143
Albi Bryant (7)   144
Georgiana Hume (7)   145
Ren Ren Zhou (6)   146
Millie Amy Hooper-Greenhill (7)   147

Umberleigh Primary School, Umberleigh

Charlie Janisch (7)	148
Vhari Findlay-Wilson (7)	150
Ruby Mae Charlemagne (6)	152
Lily Capaldi (5)	153
Emilia Locke (5)	154

Whiteparish All Saints Primary School, Whiteparish

Oliver Lewis (7)	155
Seren Elder (7)	156
Ella Davidson (6)	158
Lottie Shutler (7)	160
Sophie Martin (6)	161
Alfie Greig Hatch (7)	162
Jack Bryant (6)	163
Rosie Leach (5)	164

Whitleigh Community Primary School, Whitleigh

Jessica Rose Vicary (7)	165
Emmie Louise Thomas (7)	166
Winner Bazinga (6)	167
Dexter Robertson (7)	168
Jayden Pean (7)	169
Jacob Ackland (6)	170

The
Diaries

Dear Diary

There was a heatwave today and I had lots of fun with my friends! First, I had a swimming lesson, then I went to football, which is my favourite sport. I was awarded 'player of the day' for being a good, brave goalkeeper. Hector was trying to score a goal and kicked the ball and it smacked against my leg! It really hurt! I was brave because I carried on even though it hurt.

It was baking hot in the afternoon, so I went with my friends, William and Ellie, to the lake. They are twins and I have known them for seven years. The water was freezing, but we made up a new game of hand football. We got soaking wet, but I won the game so I was happy!

It was sweltering, so Mum bought us all an ice cream. We then had a quick play in the play area before heading home for tea. What a day!

Thomas Rhys Williams (7)

Ampney Crucis CE Primary School, Ampney Crucis

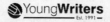

Dear Diary

I went to the park on Wednesday with my family. I met my best friend there. They told me they went to space and they said they met a monster.
After they told me the story about space, we started to play football.
Once we finished the game, we went to a café and had a chocolate milkshake and a plate of chips. We went home and played on the Wii.
We went shopping. I bought some smoothies and some slime. We went to the funfair and there were lots of animals doing tricks and people doing magic. It smelt like the zoo. There were also lots of rides, such as roller coasters and a big wheel. We could hear the music from the merry-go-round and the laughter of the children as they went up and down on the merry-go-round.

Then came a monster and two superheroes with a special potion called Dragon Potion. My best friend drank the Dragon Potion and then turned into a Pokémon called Ball of Flame. There was a flash of light and the superheroes, the monster and my Pokémon friend disappeared into a new dimension!

Nathan Smith (7)

Ampney Crucis CE Primary School, Ampney Crucis

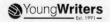
Dear Diary

It was a cold, dark night and the moon was shining down. I was with Finley and Max. We are three doggy friends. We ran away from our homes at bedtime and into the forest. When we were in the forest, we met underneath our favourite tall tree. There was a little brown door at the bottom of the tree with a golden handle. I opened the door and we all went inside. The door was a portal to a different world called Wizard World.

Inside the new world, it was a sunny day. We scampered across the green grass. Three pixies came along. They had wands in their hands and magic dust in golden bags across their shoulders. They threw the magic dust at us. The whole sky lit up with sparkles and rainbows. Hundreds of tiny fairies, wizards and pixies flew across the sky. We looked down and we all had magic doggy capes on. I had a green cape with a 'Z' on the front.

Finley had a red cape and Max had a blue cape. We had been turned into superhero dogs!

Zac Jackson (7)
Ampney Crucis CE Primary School, Ampney Crucis

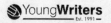

Dear Diary

Last Christmas in Fiji, my family went to a place called Udu. It was one of the most beautiful places I have ever seen.
One sunny morning, my father asked my brother and I if we wanted to go fishing and snorkelling. Sadly, my brother didn't want to go, so I went snorkelling with my dad and I felt like a fish. I wore flippers on my feet, snorkels and goggles on my face. I loved to see the fish and coral on the reef. It was colourful and the fish looked like coloured candy in the sea. We saw some little red fish and some little blue fish that had yellow fins and tails. There was a clownfish and some black and white fish.
After that, we swam back. The beach looked like brown sugar. My dad and I then went home for some delicious lunch.

Alick Nasilasila (7)
Ampney Crucis CE Primary School, Ampney Crucis

Dear Diary

Yesterday, I swam in the sparkling deep lake. It was warm and really fun. I put my purple flippers on and my blue goggles on as well. I did that at 8:30. Then me and my older sister went to the other side of the lake and walked around a bit.

When we got back, we went for a picnic. I had a ham sandwich with butter.

The next day, I went to school. I did maths and English, then I had assembly. After assembly, it was playtime. I played football. My team was Nate, Sophie, Alfie and Alick. We won 8-5.

After school, I made green slime. I stretched it really far. Then I played puppies in the tent with my sisters. After that, I had lunch. It was a margherita pizza. Then I had a pear and for pudding, I had a choc ice.

Tatty Mackenzie-Hill (7)

Ampney Crucis CE Primary School, Ampney Crucis

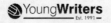

Dear Diary

You won't believe what happened to me today. I have been wishing for a puppy for so long.

I went in the dark woods and I found a puppy! I was so excited and happy. I showed my mum and dad and they were excited and happy too. It had a beautiful collar. I loved it so much.

Then the puppy got lost. I was worried. I cried and cried. When I searched in my house for the puppy, I could hear a sound. I stopped crying. It sounded like a puppy crying. I went outside and the puppy was caught in a rope. I got the puppy out and she licked me on the cheek. I named the puppy Grace.

I love playing with Grace. Mum and dad love her too... oh, and my brother.

At night, I keep Grace in a kennel.

Indya Grace McGregor (7)

Ampney Crucis CE Primary School, Ampney Crucis

Dear Diary

My friends went swimming with me and we played volleyball. After, we played mermaids and it was fun. "We've had lots of fun," said May. We played lots of games. "We've had lots of fun today," said Flo. "Let's play more games, just one more game."
"Relax! Okay," said May.
We went to Flo's home and we had a sleepover. We had lots of sweets. "Yum!" said Flo.
May said, "Yay, this is going to be the best sleepover!"
We watched the TV and watched Netflix and put on make-up and did our nails. Then we made cupcakes and candyfloss. Then we put icing on the cupcakes, and they were yummy.

Ella Lazauska (6)

Ampney Crucis CE Primary School, Ampney Crucis

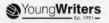
Dear Diary

I went to the zoo with my family and saw lots of animals. I saw a lot of very grey elephants and their babies too. I saw a giraffe with a few spots and it was the tallest thing I had ever seen. I saw the most beautiful horse on the planet and it was tiny. We saw pigs that were snorting and cows that were eating the grass. We fed the greedy goats and they ate the food so fast! We saw tigers which ran away in a flash and I saw a lion that was fierce and angry. We enjoyed going to the zoo because it was a sunny day. I think we should go to the zoo again. Next time we should have lunch at the zoo because it was such fun.

Rose Johnston (6)
Ampney Crucis CE Primary School, Ampney Crucis

Dear Diary

It is finally Boy's Day! Mum has had Mother's Day. Dad has had Father's Day. I decided today should be all about me! My brother, Tom, came over and we went to Airborne in Cheltenham, which is a trampoline park. We played as ninjas and jumped off the terrifying staircase onto the big pillow below. The air went up as we went down. Then we went to Smyths and bought a Pikachu teddy and some Pokémon action figures. After Five Guys, Tom felt queasy as he'd eaten two burgers!
We went home and played Team Sonic Racing until it was time for bed. I dreamt about me and Pikachu. It was the best day ever!

Harley McEwan (6)

Ampney Crucis CE Primary School, Ampney Crucis

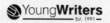
Dear Diary

Today, I went to cricket training and I hit the ball so far with just one stump. Then Charlie, Mummy and I went to the yard. We did lots of things and Charlie and I washed Mummy's car and trailer.
We then went to Charlie's presentation. I got a packet of crisps and Charlie got a medal saying 'North Wilts Youth Football League' or NWYFL for short. It was so cool. I played on my guitar and Roi was very impressed. Later, I went swimming and did multi-sports.

Sophie Laura Cook (7)

Ampney Crucis CE Primary School, Ampney Crucis

Dear Diary

On Saturday, I went to a football match with a monster. England scored two goals. The monster jumped into the game and he scored ten goals. Everyone was scared of the green monster because he didn't have any teeth and he only had one eye. He got hungry and angry, so he looked for some food. He found some food behind glass, so he smashed the glass. Then he went to prison.

Henry James Clapton (6)
Ampney Crucis CE Primary School, Ampney Crucis

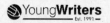

Dear Diary

A monster was on the moon. It was the boss monster! It was dangerous. I didn't like it! I didn't know what to do. In the distance, there was a superhero. He saved me. I was in a zoo, the superhero saved me. Then I was in the park. My best friends were there and my family. I went to the funfair! It was much better.

Guy Sparrow (6)
Ampney Crucis CE Primary School, Ampney Crucis

Dear Diary

I have had the best day of my life! I went to Mars and played moonball with the aliens and I won! I also found out where they live and they live in the core of the moon. I went on an adventure and it was so cool and weird because I couldn't understand them. After that, I travelled with the aliens to their planet and it was super cool and there was a radioactive plant. It stank, ew! After all of that, I felt so hungry and I ate so much moon cheese and it was good! We then went to the moon again. Then the aliens teleported me to a diamond planet and it was so cool because it was made completely out of solid diamond.
The aliens then took me back to my spaceship and I felt so happy. I had finally been to space. I said goodbye to the aliens and I felt sad for them. I went back on my spaceship and felt so happy!

Corey Woods

Chesterton Primary School, Chesterton

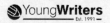

Dear Diary

I have had the most exciting day ever! I went to the funfair with my two friends, Molly and Sarah. We bought three tickets. When we got there, we saw about two hundred rides and we also saw signs that said: *Open twenty-four hours a day!* There was the biggest, cheapest and yummiest candyfloss ever! The best part was if you ate too much candy, you would never get sick. We could hear burgers sizzling and I could taste tomato ketchup in the air running in my mouth.

First, we all went on a roller coaster as fast as a rocket with extra fire. Then me and Molly went to eat a burger with tomato ketchup, bacon, salad and cheese. Sarah couldn't eat a burger because she had new braces. After mine and Molly's food went down, we went on the Ferris wheel. Then suddenly, we got stuck up at the very top!

After two hours, we finally got down. Afterwards, we chilled out. When we were on the Ferris wheel, I felt really sick because we were very high. On the roller coaster, I felt scared because it went really quick.
On the way back, the seat felt really smooth and silky. On the bus, I felt sleepy because we'd had a long day.
As soon as we got home, we fell asleep on the floor with our clothes on. We slept until 1pm.

Madison Indie Griffin (8)
Chesterton Primary School, Chesterton

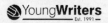

Dear Diary

Today was the greatest day of my life! Me, Olivia and Sophie went to the park and had so much fun! We saw playing equipment and ice cream vans. I got a sloppy Slushie and crackling candyfloss. It all cost £3.80! We all had lots of fun in the shop. We all bought three plush toys each. I got elephants, Olivia got cheetahs and Sophie got bunnies. We played on the equipment. We all enjoyed the swings and the slide, but what we all liked most was when we climbed trees, especially when we cannonballed into a pile of leaves. We then stopped for sweet treats. They were delicious.

Next, it was time for lunch. For lunch, we had strawberry jam sandwiches with ready salted crisps. We loved it! After that, we all sunbathed and me and Olivia raced each other. I won two and Olivia won two, which meant it was a tie.

Finally, we all went home. I was so happy and excited when we sunbathed. I got tanned. I've had a wonderful day, but I'm a bit tired, so I'm going to bed.

Connie Dearman (8)

Chesterton Primary School, Chesterton

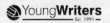

Dear Diary

Today, I have had an outstanding day at the funfair. I spent ages at the funfair because it was amazing. I took my friends, Alaha and Elsia, so I could go on rides with them. It was awesome! I could see bright lights, spinny roller coasters, popping popcorn, hot dogs sizzling, snow cones freezing, candyfloss, waffles and fresh doughnuts. I could smell the fresh grass and the lovely breeze.

I went on the scariest ride there, but first I bought a ticket. I had a burger for lunch and also watched people on other rides. I laughed at people on rides.

I was exhausted at the end of the day because I went on lots of rides. I felt excited when I got home, but I was bored when I was just sat down. I was very scared when I was going on scary rides. I was hyper when I was eating yummy, scrumptious sweets.

I always get hyper when I eat yummy, scrumptious sweets.
I have had a wonderful day, but now I have to go to bed.

Summer Magson (8)

Chesterton Primary School, Chesterton

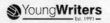

Dear Diary

Today, I've had the best day of my life! I went to the fair with my sister Chloe, my mum, dad, Jessica and Nanny Kay. First, I went on massive roller coasters. It felt very weird. I could hear people screaming. It was so fun! When that was over, I went on one that went really high and then dropped five times. It was very scary. After that, I went on one that shot back and forth ten times so you could see the ground and sky. Next, I went on the Ferris wheel. It was white with blue carts and yellow seats. It was so fun! I went on it twice. I had two hot dogs for lunch. It was great! After that, I ate a lot of popcorn with sugar sprinkled on top. It was delicious. Then I had candyfloss. It smelt great. At the end, I went on more roller coasters. I loved them all. After, I asked if we could go again. I love the funfair!

On the way home, I was full of joy but also tired, so when I got home, I went to bed.

Evie Amsden (8)

Chesterton Primary School, Chesterton

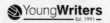

Dear Diary

I've had the most awesome day of my life! It all started when I went to the funfair with Spider-Man and Batman. I could smell the popcorn scent. I could hear the sizzling of the meat. I could see the blazing of the lights and I could touch the thin air.
We went to buy some tickets for some rides. We tried all of them, even The End. For those of you that don't know what The End is, I'll tell you now. The End is a dark and gloomy ride. It has these tall-looking creatures called Endermen. Endermen can teleport. The End is mostly purple. It has obsidian pillars that have End crystals on top. The last and hardest thing to do is to kill the Ender dragon. For bonus points, shoot Endermen. The aim of the game is to kill the Ender dragon. The one who kills the Ender dragon is the winner.

Liam Painter (8)
Chesterton Primary School, Chesterton

Dear Diary

I had the most wonderful day ever. I went to the funfair. Before I went, I chose who I wanted to go with: Nanny, Mummy, Grandad and Big Gran.

When we got there, we got the tickets and I heard people screaming on roller coasters. When I was on my way to get a burger, I smelt popcorn popping.

At the funfair, on the Ferris wheel, I saw bright lights. I went on a roller coaster ride and I was screaming so loud because it was high and scary. Then I went on some other rides and did some activities. My favourite activity was face painting. When I walked into the funfair, at first, I was so nervous. Then I got more into it and felt happy, excited and joyful.

I had a good day at the funfair, now I am off to bed.

Riley Paget (8)

Chesterton Primary School, Chesterton

Dear Diary

Yesterday, I asked my mum if I could go to the zoo and she said yes. When we got there, we saw some snakes and tarantulas. We went on a train ride. We saw zebras. Then we had lunch.

After, we saw some penguins. They got fed fish and then went under the water. Then we saw amazing lions and giraffes. Next, we saw some rhinos and they smelt like rotten eggs. We stopped for a break and then saw some jet-black gorillas. We saw some deer with their mum. I could smell burgers.

On my way home, I felt happy because I had seen so many great animals.

Emrisson Latham
Chesterton Primary School, Chesterton

Dear Diary

I had the most epic day at the funfair. I went with my dog called Max.
When we arrived, we bought some tickets. We could smell sausages sizzling on the cooker. We went on some rides. One of the rides was a roller coaster. It was very scary. We also went on another ride. It was called Haunted House. It was terrifying because ghosts jumped out at you. Then we had a picnic. After that, we went on the dodgems. Then we watched a show and there were fireworks. Then we went home.
I've had a great day, but now I am off to bed.

Charlie Elwell (8)
Chesterton Primary School, Chesterton

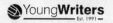
Dear Diary

I had the most exciting day at the funfair. I went with my friends Joe, Jack and Garry. We went on the Ferris wheel and had some hot dogs. We had so much fun. I had a big, juicy hot dog for lunch. We smelt sizzling hot dogs, heard people screaming and saw blazing red-hot lights. We went on some more rides. We went on the bumper cars and the roller coaster. After, we felt sick! On the way home, we played some air guitars and we felt very, very happy and very excited. I had lots of fun.
Goodnight, Diary.

Harrison Dearman (8)
Chesterton Primary School, Chesterton

Dear Diary

I had the most lovely day. I went with my mummy and daddy and my sister to the zoo.

When I got there, I could hear lots of the animals. First, we saw the lions and they were scary.

At 12 o'clock, we had lunch. I ate a king-sized burger and it was so delicious. Then we saw the stinky giraffes and the rhinos. The rhinos were sunbathing because it was so hot.

We got in the car and went home. I felt really good because the zoo was so fun. I went to bed because all the excitement had tired me out.

Cayden Scrivens (8)

Chesterton Primary School, Chesterton

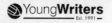
Dear Diary

I had a wonderful day at the zoo with my mum and brother. We spent the whole day at the zoo. It was amazing!

When we arrived, I couldn't believe what I saw! Rhinos and hippos! They were really big and made me a bit nervous. Then we went to see the fuzzy penguins.

At ten o'clock, we ate lunch. I had a sandwich that was delicious and I had some strawberries and an apple and a chewy bar. Then I played in the park.

On the way back, I was tired and when we got home, we had tea in bed.

Katelyn Mummery (8)
Chesterton Primary School, Chesterton

Dear Diary

I had the most extraordinary day ever... I went to space! First, we climbed into the rocket and flew into space. We nearly crashed into a space asteroid. I went with Holly the dog and Yellow the duck.

We arrived there and I saw the nine planets: Mercury, Venus, Earth, Mars, Jupiter, Saturn, Uranus, Neptune and Pluto. Soon, I learned about how hot the planets were. Then we went on a moonwalk.

Finally, we had lunch in the rocket and went home. I was sad to leave space but maybe we can go again.

Lisa Fernando (8)

Chesterton Primary School, Chesterton

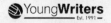
Dear Diary

I have had the best day ever, it was so sunny. I said to Mum, "Can we go to the park?"
We went to the park and played on the swing. Then Mum let me and Ben ride our bikes around the park. Then we went on the roundabout and then the slide.
Next, we had a picnic. I could smell the ham sandwich. For pudding, we had ice cream. We were all exhausted and Mum said we had to go home. We had all had an amazing day.

Charlie Smith (8)
Chesterton Primary School, Chesterton

Dear Diary

Today, I went to the funfair with my super friend, Freddie. We went for a ride on the roller coaster. Then we had lunch. We had a hot dog and burgers. I then went on the bumper cars and after that, I went to see a magic show.
Then we went home and I was so tired I went to sleep.

Sophia Coll (8)

Chesterton Primary School, Chesterton

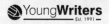

Dear Diary

Last week was Art Week. I made my own creation out of recyclable materials. This creation is a dinosaur from Planet Mars! My dinosaur likes space things and loves doing things on his spaceship. I loved making my dinosaur creation. I have helped to save the planet by using recyclable materials. I used a dinosaur mould, cups, googly eyes, pipe cleaners and pom-poms. I hope I can make another creation soon.

Maggie Shanley (10)
Linwood School, Bournemouth

Dear Diary

Last week was Art Week. I made a rocket out of recycled materials. I used a cardboard coffee cup, string, a little bit of metal, straws and pipe cleaners. I also used a cardboard container and some plastic. I used a glue gun and normal glue to stick it all together.

Dexter Bond (9)

Linwood School, Bournemouth

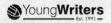
Dear Diary

On Saturday, I went to the beach with my family. There were so many people on the beach. I was swimming in the sea. We had a great time. We had a snack there and I drank water. I played games on the beach. It was fun. I played volleyball.

Bruno Henriaues (11)
Linwood School, Bournemouth

Dear Diary

Last week, we had Art Week. I painted a dinosaur with the colour green. The dinosaur was a T-rex. I made a robot T-rex with a big cup and little cups. My dinosaur is a rocket and it is a rocket robot T-rex.

Achintya Tirumala (9)

Linwood School, Bournemouth

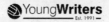

Dear Diary

On Sunday, I went to the cinema to meet Victor and Charlie. We saw 'Toy Story 4'. I ate popcorn with Oreos. Victor had the same and Charlie had a Slushie. We all saw VR. And that was my Sunday.

Matthew Biggs (10)
Linwood School, Bournemouth

Dear Diary

Last week, we had Art Week. In Art Week, we went swimming. I painted aeroplanes and when they were broken, I used glue.

Adam Long (11)

Linwood School, Bournemouth

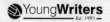
Dear Diary

On Saturday, I went to Marwell Zoo with my family and cousins. We saw tarantulas, tigers, dinosaur statues and monkeys.

Aaron Davis (11)
Linwood School, Bournemouth

Dear Diary

I went to the beach with my friend, Kamila. We played football and made sandcastles. We splashed in the sea.

Gabi Oskar Izydorczyk (10)

Linwood School, Bournemouth

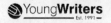
Dear Diary

Last week, me, my mum and my smelly sister went to the Cheltenham Science Festival. We went to Recipes of Wonder. It was so cool. We got to make a balloon-powered car, banging paper and a paper helicopter. We also had a race with the balloon-powered cars! Then we went to a big building and a man talked to us about science.

After that, we went to a place where people were doing circus acts. We did plate spinning. We went on the stilts and I went on a unicycle.

Not long after that, we went to Incredible Insects and Beastly Bugs. Now that was funny! After, we went to Wagamama. Me and my sister had cod bites. They were yummy!

When we got home, we had dinner, sat on the sofa and watched TV. Finally, we went to bed.

Elodie Jackson (7)
Parkend Primary School, Parkend

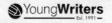

Dear Diary

Last Monday, I went to the funfair. I went with my mum, dad and my sister. First, I went to see the tigers and giraffes, but I had to wait in a queue. It took 50 minutes. After I went to the cage, I had a sandwich, Tango and crisps. We set up a tent. It took 15 minutes. We had a bag of marshmallows on the campfire at 7 o'clock.
When we woke up, we went to the shop. I bought a teddy which cost £7. It was a tiger teddy. It was our last night. It had been good fun and we went on the rides at the funfair again. Then we went back to our campervan. It took an hour to get home. I was exhausted.
When we got home, we watched TV with popcorn, chocolate and sweets and then we went to bed.

Jack Eisel (7)
Parkend Primary School, Parkend

Dear Diary

One day, I went to a puppy centre. We saw dogs like our dog named Tara and Bella. Then we went swimming and the dog was allowed in the pool. We had a great time, but someone came in with a shark fin and we got scared. We jumped in and accidentally jumped on him and he cried. The next day was Easter. We had a good time. We had an Easter hunt. I found the most. My dad told us about a monster who eats chocolate at Easter. My sister got scared. Dad said it was just made up.
I asked if I could go to my friend's house. On the way, I got scared. I heard something say, "I am going to eat your chocolate..."

Zaya-Mae Phelps-Hall (7)
Parkend Primary School, Parkend

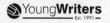

Dear Diary

One day, I went go-karting with my dad. We had to wear a go-kart helmet and clothes. After, we had to queue up. Luckily, me and my dad were at the front of the queue. Soon, we got in a double-seated cart. Then the man turned the engine on and got it started. When we went on the track, I decided I would steer and my dad pushed the peddles. When we went around a corner, we did a three-sixty! At the end, we missed the turning, so we went round again and turned in. We took the clothes off. On the way there, we saw a park, so we went to the park. When we went home, we played and went to bed.

Indie Sparks (7)
Parkend Primary School, Parkend

Dear Diary

The best day of my life was when I went to the zoo. I had lots of fun. I loved the penguins and giraffes the best. I saw llamas, lions and howler monkeys. I feel like the howler monkeys should be called growler monkeys because they growl. I went on a tour thing as well. I went to a café and got a milkshake, then I went to see the meerkats. I went to see the pandas after. After I had seen all the animals, I went home. I played on my Nintendo Switch. Later, I had tea and then I watched YouTube.

Idris Rontree Jones (6)

Parkend Primary School, Parkend

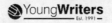
Dear Diary

It was nearly my birthday, so I went to the zoo. I saw African penguins and a lion and also some fish. Then I left and went home. The next day was my birthday. I was six and I had cake and it was fun.

It was nearly Christmas. I went to play with lots of animals. My dad said we would get a cat in five sleeps.

Then it was Christmas. I had lots of presents and I couldn't wait as this was the day I got a cat. I was so happy and played with him. I called him Monty. I love him so much.

Sahana Waller (6)

Parkend Primary School, Parkend

Dear Diary

Yesterday, I went to the funfair with my family. We had a milkshake and slimy sweets. We had so much fun.

When we got home, we went to bed. I had a bedtime story about a family. After we had the story, we had popcorn in bed and a drink of water. We got our cuddly teddies and got back into bed.

When we woke up, we had Coco Pops for breakfast and then we watched television. We then brushed our teeth and got dressed. Then we played in the garden.

Milly Tillings (6)

Parkend Primary School, Parkend

Dear Diary

I went to the park with my sister and my mum. I played on the slide and then we got lunch.

At KFC, I had bits of chicken and chips. Then we went shopping. I got some sweets.

When we got home, we got the dog and went for a walk. He ran around and around. When we finally got home, we took our shoes off and watched a movie, 'Captain Underpants'. After that, we ate dinner and went to sleep. I had a dream about my cats.

Willow Rose Brown (7)
Parkend Primary School, Parkend

Dear Diary

I went to the zoo with my family. It was good. First, I saw the elephants. They were big and funny and they were fantastic. Then we went to see the baboons. They were funny and silly. They were climbing the trees and they were really funny. They were really furry and they had red bottoms and had silly heads. The baby ones were small and the big ones were funny.

Alby Arnold (6)

Parkend Primary School, Parkend

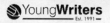

Dear Diary

Yesterday, I went to the amazing zoo and I had a strawberry ice cream with a flake. I went to see a giraffe and a panda. It was very hot, so we went on the water slides. Then I had lunch.
It was nearly time to go, so we went to the car and went home.
When I got home, I went to bed.

Daisy Baldwin (6)
Parkend Primary School, Parkend

Dear Diary

I went to space and saw an alien. I found myself on Planet Googoo. It was humongous. I went exploring. I found a machine that aliens had destroyed. I made a spaceship and blew the planet up.
I went home and ate ice cream and played Plants vs Zombies. I played with my dad and I won.

Reuben-Kai Williams (6)

Parkend Primary School, Parkend

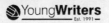

Dear Diary

I went to the park. I played on the swing and the slide and the monkey bars. I also played in the sandpit with my mum, my dad, my nan, my dog and my cats. I bought a unicorn. Then we went home. I watched a film and then went to bed.

Maia Walters (7)
Parkend Primary School, Parkend

Dear Diary

I went to the park and I went on the slide. I slid down the slide. Then I went on the monkey bars. I went on the swings and then I went to the grown-up slide and the grown-up swings.

Ava Harrison (6)

Parkend Primary School, Parkend

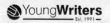

Dear Diary

I went to Florence and Letti's birthday party with my family. We went there at 11 o'clock to set up. Me, Florence and Letti bounced on the trampoline. We also went up to Letti's bedroom and went on her bunkbed. Then at 1 o'clock, the party started and everybody came through the gate, Spike came first, then the rest. First, we played eat strawberry laces off the washing line, who eats it first then gets a prize. Next, we did a great fabulous egg and spoon race. On the second go, we had to hold it with our teeth. After, we got to eat the chocolate egg. We played duck, duck, goose and Letti started, she picked Spike. Letti didn't get tagged, instead, the beautiful girl kept running. Then we played pass the parcel, Letti and Florence started. I got chocolate. The parcel was over, fifteen magic tricks in a teeny tiny box. Heidi and Edward won them.

Amelie Passmore (6)

Salway Ash CE (VA) Primary School, Salway Ash

Dear Diary

I went to Womad on my special birthday. I took Lois and Eve my BFFs forever. One evening, we saw a rainbow unicorn fairy, she had sparkling eyes like diamonds. The magic unicorn fairy said, "Who are you?"
"My name is Bella and these are my BFFs, Eve and Lois."
"Do you want to see my BFFs?" the unicorn said.
I said, "Yes, please!"
"You need to go on the dashing unicorn train, choo, choo."
"Do you need to pay for this ride?"
"No, it's fun for free!" the fairy said in a nice voice. She said, "Wave, this is my home."
"It looks like my home, where are you from?"
"Up and up, in Heaven."

Bella Huxter (7)
Salway Ash CE (VA) Primary School, Salway Ash

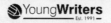
Dear Diary

On Sunday, I went to Burton Bradstock Beach and had some lovely fish and chips. After that, we made a sandcastle, but it didn't completely work so we went to the sea to get some water. My little sister wanted to go deep-sea diving and she got all wet so we had to change her.
Next, I had to dig a hole and I put the water in the hole and gave it a mix with my dirty spade and put it in my new bucket and tipped it up and it fell a bit so we tried again. It was better. We went down to the sea and got our feet wet.
At last, we had ice cream. I had bubble gum ice cream and my sister had vanilla ice cream. Then we went home for supper.

Felicity Rogers (7)
Salway Ash CE (VA) Primary School, Salway Ash

Dear Diary

I went to busy LegoLand. I went with my mum. It was a two-and-a-half-hour moody car journey to LegoLand.

We went on twenty rides, I went on the Fiat Driving School. I went on it four times. The first time, I had a yellow car and the next three, I got a red car, that was my favourite ride. We were there all day. The mini city was mini but Big Ben and other big things were taller than my parents.

In the big Lego shop, I bought a megalodon and a Lego police car. There was only one little shower. I loved LegoLand.

William Bowditch (7)
Salway Ash CE (VA) Primary School, Salway Ash

Dear Diary

I went to the zoo with my mum called Wendy and my dad called Tim and my brother called Harry. At the zoo, I saw a waddling penguin, then it was lunchtime. I had a few sweets with my lunch.
After lunch, I caught a Pokémon and its name was Pikachu and he was yellow and black. After, I went back home and went shopping. Then I went to a brilliant park with my brother Harry. I went home and had dinner and then read a story and I went to bed.

Guy Holloway Huxford (6)
Salway Ash CE (VA) Primary School, Salway Ash

Dear Diary

I went to space with my amazing superhero and when we got there, we played football. Then we saw an alien next to the space rocket calling to another alien. They looked like people with big horns and their eyes were on top of their horns. Then they went into the rocket, but my superhero was just in time and stopped the door closing. The superhero asked if they could help us get back to our house. The aliens said yes.

William Joy (7)
Salway Ash CE (VA) Primary School, Salway Ash

Dear Diary

I went to the funfair with a monster. We went on the fastest ride and then we played Pokémon, Spider-Man and Sonic.
We went to the shops, I got a robot toy. We went to the games, I played Minecraft. I made a house, it was made out of black wood and my pets were a sheep and a dog. We played Wreck-It Ralph, then Minecraft again and made a fishing stand.

Charlie Joce (7)
Salway Ash CE (VA) Primary School, Salway Ash

Dear Diary

I went to the Disney park and played at the parks. I saw Mickey and his friends. I had an ice cream, a doughnut and a steak. I had a special cake and saw Minnie and went on a ride called Woody Woodpecker. I saw a giraffe.

Sivatia Goligher (6)

Salway Ash CE (VA) Primary School, Salway Ash

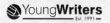
Dear Diary

Yesterday, I went to a place. No ordinary place, but a place where I got my pet griffin, Iceshard. Iceshard and I swerved through the winter forest covered with snow. Then we started to see little snow fairies called Ruby, Amber, Saffron, Fern, Sky, Izzy, Heather, Polly, Ally, Flora and Tinker Bell and many more. We even saw Peter Pan, who welcomed us!

Finally, we came to Griffin World. Its entrance was sealed up and all the fairies disappeared. I forgot to tell you Flare came along too. He is an alicorn, like Pokémon Rapidash. We saw Iceshard and Flare's parents. Before Iceshard could zoom away and leave me behind falling, Ally, Peter Pan and Flora made me into a fairy. I saw the queen and king of griffins and the queen and king of alicorns.

I had actually come to see the Goddess of all Magnificent Creatures. I talked to her and she said, "There is no queen or king of fairies. Can you be the queen of fairies?" I said yes and with the magic of the goddess, she turned me into the Queen of Fairies. When I got back to my magical house, I told my sister all about it.

Eliana Quainoo (7)
St Joseph's RC Primary School, Highweek

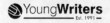

Dear Diary

At the weekend, I went to Cornwall. My mummy forgot shoes, so we went to the shop and got some shoes.

On Saturday morning, I went to Roskilly's and had breakfast. We had a little walk and after, we had ice cream.

On Saturday afternoon, I went to the beach with Posy Kiley and Brian. We went in the sea and the waves were big.

On Saturday night, me and Annie had a spa night. We had lots of treatments and we had a tray of fruit and sweets. Then we both went to bed late. I went to bed at 9 o'clock and Annie went to bed at 9:30.

On Sunday, I went to Grandma's house. I saw Brodie, my cousin. We played for a long time and after that, we went to the park and played there a bit.

Then I went home and I had Domino's for dinner. Then I watched a bit of TV and then I went to bed.

Isla McKinley (6)

St Joseph's RC Primary School, Highweek

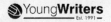

Dear Diary

On Saturday, I had a show, but it was late at night so I had to wait a long time. At least my friend, Farolld, was there. I normally just sat down in my old dance, now I am doing street dance, a little like hip-hop. In my dance, I had a hair bun, a costume and make-up. My dad thought I was beautiful. Before I had my show, we had fish and chips, but they forgot the ketchup! While I was waiting, I had a fudge cookie ice cream. Mmm, it was yummy!
Near the end of my show, we got changed. We put on our Oliver Brown T-shirts for the finale. After the finale, we put on our normal clothes.
I was very tired when I got home so I went to sleep and was happy.

Amelia Grant (7)
St Joseph's RC Primary School, Highweek

Dear Diary

Sunday, I went to Fin Lake. I went swimming and I went on the water slide.

Then I went to the park and played on the swing. Then I got booked in for dance practice.

On Monday, I came home. At home, I played in the garden. Then after dinner, I went to karate and I got my red belt. I felt happy. Then I had ballet practice. I performed the White Swan. I got good attendance.

On Tuesday, I went to Camp Bestival and there was a parade.

At home, I went in the hot tub. When it was nearly bedtime, I read my favourite book called 'Fairy Ellie'.

Evangeline Joy Peacock (6)
St Joseph's RC Primary School, Highweek

Dear Diary

Yesterday, I went to the beach with Dad, Jack and Max, my dog. I played catch with Max. It was fun. Then Jack helped me build a sandcastle. It was big. At the beach, it was hot, so I sat in the shade. Dad said, "Do you want an ice cream?"
I said yes. I had a caramel ice cream with rainbow sprinkles. It was yummy. I finished my ice cream and got dressed and went into the sea. That was my favourite bit. I got cold, so I got out of the sea. I dried off and sat down. Max buried my hat. I spent ages looking for it. I finally found it!

Annie Merrin Madeline Turner (7)
St Joseph's RC Primary School, Highweek

Dear Diary

On Saturday, I went to town and there was a festival. I stopped to see the festival until it ended.

I saw the fire engine and the ambulance. I also saw a really cool car and got a card of the car. There was a bus with people at the top throwing sweets and I got Haribo.

I felt hungry and went to Burger King next to the festival. I had a cheeseburger and my brother had chicken and fries.

When we got back outside, the festival had ended. The festival was great and we forgot to eat our sweets!

Brendon Letchford (7)

St Joseph's RC Primary School, Highweek

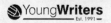
Dear Diary

I went on holiday to Majorca with Mummy and Daddy. We stayed in a hotel. We went to the swimming pool. It was cold but fun! Then we got ice cream.
The next day, we got breakfast, then we went to town, where there were trampolines and bouncy castles.
On Wednesday, we got breakfast, then went to the beach. I played in the clear blue sea. I also made a sandcastle.
We went climbing the next day.

Isla Rose Hoskin (6)
St Joseph's RC Primary School, Highweek

Dear Diary

On Saturday, I got a belt for winning a fight with the world's best Muay Thai man. I was very proud of myself. Dad was too. For a warm-up, we ran on the running machine. After that, we did some pads. I worked really hard on the pads and ended up knocking it off his hand. My mum and Aunty Katy and Maisie were proud of me. The best bit was getting the big belt!

Heidi Long (7)
St Joseph's RC Primary School, Highweek

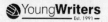

Dear Diary

A few days ago, I went to a farm. I went with my mum Ika, my dad Chris and my brother and sister Kai and Kimmy. There were so many goats. I fed one and he licked me! I also went on the tractor. I had a sandwich for lunch but the pigs ate it. I was so hungry for the rest of the visit. Luckily, I had a Burger King on the way home. That was my day!

Jessica-Jane Kneeshaw (7)
St Joseph's RC Primary School, Highweek

Dear Diary

At the weekend, I went to my cousin's. On Saturday, I went to a fair and carnival. I won a goldfish for my sister. Next, I got a balloon. I got an octopus. My sister got a turtle.
When I got home, I went in the hot tub.

Harry James Robinson (6)
St Joseph's RC Primary School, Highweek

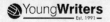

Dear Diary

I went to the beach. At the beach, there was a dead fish. I put the dead fish in the sea. I went to catch crabs. I caught seven crabs, three in the sea and four on the beach. It was a very hot day. I had lots of fun.

Filip Jaglowski (7)
St Joseph's RC Primary School, Highweek

Dear Diary

Yesterday, I went to my nan and grandad's house. They have a small swimming pool that I went in with my brothers and Isla and Immy. We played in the water, I won! We splashed about in the water. It was great fun!

Charlie Edge (7)

St Joseph's RC Primary School, Highweek

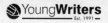

Dear Diary

Yesterday, I went to the zoo. I saw lots of animals, like elephants and penguins. Me and my brother got some toys. My favourite bit was getting ice cream. I went to the shelter to hold a pet but it was shut!

Bobbie-Rae Rawlings (7)
St Joseph's RC Primary School, Highweek

Dear Diary

I went to the arcades with my cousins. I got 197 spiky tickets and then I went on the money machine. I got some sweets, then went to the pet shop and got a fluffy cat called Fluffy Bongo.

Ellis Gillam (6)

St Joseph's RC Primary School, Highweek

Dear Diary

I went to Teignmouth Beach. I went bodyboarding. The waves pushed me really hard. I picked up shells.
When I got home, I looked at them. It was a really good day.

Robin Jack Harris (7)
St Joseph's RC Primary School, Highweek

Dear Diary

Yesterday, I went fishing with Daddy. We caught three catfish and two dotted fish. Dad cut the fish and Mummy cooked it. I had a great time fishing.

Michael Hooper (7)
St Joseph's RC Primary School, Highweek

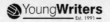
Dear Diary

I went to the swimming pool. I didn't have any armbands. I went to the wavy pool. I jumped in a big wave and my mum screamed.

Grace Stoyle (6)
St Joseph's RC Primary School, Highweek

Dear Diary

Yesterday, I went swimming with my family. We didn't like one of the pools, so we went to the wavy pool. There were lots of slides. There was a great slide. Me and my brother went down it. Our sisters didn't go down because they don't like straight slides. They went down a different slide.

My dad went on the diving board, but he splashed and got my nan wet. My mum got in the hot tub when I was in the hot tub but it was cold so she got out of the hot tub. The pool was hot, so she stayed in the pool. The pool had seats around the outside. There was a really high slide where you had to use a floaty that had two holes in it. My brother sat in front of me. I sat behind him because I was scared.

After it stopped, we went on a slide. They pressed a button and then we had to swim to the baby side of the pool.

Sophia Peddle (7)

St Mark's VA Primary School, Worle

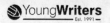
Dear Diary

A month or two ago, I went to space with a unicorn. I know right! A unicorn, that's crazy! But it wasn't any type of unicorn, it was a kind of space unicorn. The unicorn couldn't die. It came to land about 100 years ago. The unicorn's name is Maddy Unicorn.

She had been trying to find only one person to go to space with her, then she found me! I did forget to tell you Maddy is a very shy unicorn. She won't talk to strangers or anything.

Maddy wanted me to go to space with her. Maddy whispered to me and told me that her unicorn family lived there. Her mummy, Leah, her daddy, Dave, her sister, Annabelle, and her brother, Freddie.

"Oh wow!" I said. "You've got a nice big family."

"I know," said Maddy. " A nice, big, wonderful, special, normal family. Let's go to space now."
"But how are we going to get there?" I said.
"Oh!" said Maddy. "Don't worry, I can fly. Off we go!"
It took about 260 minutes to get there.
When we arrived, it was fun. "Hello, Maddy," everyone said.
We all lived happily ever after.

Bobbi Morley (7)
St Mark's VA Primary School, Worle

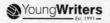

Dear Diary

Today, I woke up and I had teleported to an island. On the island next to me there was a wizard! He said he was from the oldest island alive.

After a while, I found four Poké Balls. I chose a Mewtwo and a Dragonite. After I picked up the Poké Balls, I was trapped in a cage. I shouted for the wizard but all I could see was a skull. In the skull, there was a map. When I opened the map, a portal appeared that went to the wizard. I showed him the map. He told the Dragonite where to go. The wizard led me to the X marks the spot and the Mewtwo created a tough shovel to get in. Inside was a treasure chest! I had to put in the skull to open it, but the wizard created a lockpick to pick the lock. It opened! Inside was millions of gold coins and lots of diamonds. There was a mythical block. When I touched the block, the wizard died.

I got his powers and I bought him back to life. I gave him some power and I lived with him. The block made me twenty-five years older.

Oliver Rogers (7)
St Mark's VA Primary School, Worle

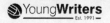

Dear Diary

Yesterday, I went to Unicorn World with my mum and dad. I saw unicorns running in the meadow. I was allowed to decorate a real-life one. It was fun. I had a unicorn ice cream, it was really sunny!
I watched 'Secret Life of Unicorns 2', it was really funny. I rode a unicorn and it did a trick. It was great fun.
Me and Dad went on a unicorn ride. It spun around and Daddy felt sick, but I didn't. It was amazing. Then I plaited a unicorn's hair. It was really fun. I went into a unicorn class. I saw a glass window unicorn on the window. I was amazed.
I went to a unicorn club, it was an art and crafts club. I made a papier mâché unicorn. My mum and dad loved it and I loved it too. It was a long journey home. I had to go on an aeroplane for two hours, then I had to go on a train, then another aeroplane and

then a bus for an hour.

Finally, I got in the car, but before I left, I got given a unicorn goodie bag and it was yummy.

Ezmee Bobbin (7)
St Mark's VA Primary School, Worle

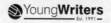
Dear Diary

I went to the park with Erin, Lara, Ezme and Bella. It was very hot and sunny so we wore shorts and a vest, but then it went cold and snowed. We went to the shops to get five sledges. We did five races and everyone won one race each. We did one more race and I won a lollipop. We then all had a chocolate milkshake. Me and Ezme had a Twix.
Bella and Lara then went on the roundabout. We then danced and did gymnastics. We met another friend called Kate. Kate has one sister called Molly and one brother called Joe. We played with all of them. First, we played tag and hide-and-seek. Then we climbed to the top of the tree. We all played a game where you have to climb to the top of the tree in sixty seconds. Me and Ezme made it but the rest didn't make it.

Then we found Olivia and we got a hot tub and ten swimsuits so we went in it. As soon as we got in, it was very hot. I asked if everyone got in, everyone said yes. It was the best day ever.

Emily Wellsbury (7)

St Mark's VA Primary School, Worle

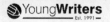
Dear Diary

On Sunday, I went to the zoo! I went with Batman and Superman. I went in the awesome park! I saw Pac-Man. He flew all over the place. We saw a huge lion that was red and his orange mane was really fluffy. It was sunny and hot. I got an ice cream and Batman said to Superman, "There's Spider-Man. Let's tell him what we are doing and ask him how to get Woody a superhero." I heard but I didn't say anything.

On the way to the monkeys, I saw a crocodile and a leopard. We had a talk to Spider-Man. We saw Dexter and a policeman, a unicorn, zebra, dragon, tiger and an enormous cage that was the size of an elephant. I think I met a zookeeper and she told me that the cage was for a new animal. I crept off so I could have a party, but not for long, because Superman was sad that I had gone. He told Batman and they both came looking for me.

When they found me, I was super upset because I was having a great time.

Woody Milton (7)

St Mark's VA Primary School, Worle

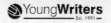

Dear Diary

Today, we went to the zoo. I was really excited to see the cute animals. I walked inside and the first animal I saw was a green snake in the tree. Then we walked along a path and saw another animal. It was a green turtle under the water.

After that, we had lunch. I had a burger and a Sprite. After lunch, we went to the zebras and then we walked to see the parrots and the ladybirds. Far away, there were cows in the barn and sheep. There were grey elephants. They were squirting out of their trunks.

The next thing we saw was a monkey swinging in the trees. Next to him was a chimp in the tree too. In quite a lot more steps, we saw alligators. They were snapping their teeth at me.

Then we went to have an ice cream! Then we saw a kangaroo jumping.

After the kangaroos, we saw a sloth in a tree. Then we went to see the grey hippos and the fish. Then I saw a hamster running on a wheel. Then I saw a brown rabbit.

Dexter Cunningham (7)

St Mark's VA Primary School, Worle

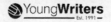
Dear Diary

It was the day we went to the beach. "Yay!"
I said.
I went to my mum's room and woke her up.
Then she said, "Let's get ready to go to the
beach."
When we got there, we saw an ice cream
truck. We bought an ice cream, then I saw a
mermaid. She was a beautiful mermaid. She
had a beautiful purple tail. I swam over to
the rock and met her. Then we built a
mermaid castle with sand. It was the best
day ever.
Then I met the king of the sea. He was a
very nice king. Then a man said, "Who is
this?"
I said, "My name is Annabelle."
He said, "What a nice name. Do you want
me to show you the sea?"

I said, "Yes."
We saw the king's bedroom, it was very nice. Then I swam up to the shore and said, "I will be back soon!" Then I went home. I watched TV, then I went to bed and slept and dreamed of candy and candy trees.

Annabelle Tonkinson (7)
St Mark's VA Primary School, Worle

Dear Diary

You'll never guess what I did on my most exciting day ever! I went to a theme park called Woodlands! It was my holiday when I went. On the way there, I saw a lot of cars. We went on the motorway and then we arrived. I was so excited! The first two rides I went on was the Twister water slide and the Rapids water slide! The Twister slide was a tunnel slide and the inside was yellow and so was the outside.

When we went in the maze, I walked into a dead end. There was a scary pirate skeleton.

Finally, I reached the end of the maze. It was quite hard! The pirate ship ride was very fun. It was brown. It went up, down, up, down. I was at the very back! Finally, we went in the play area. I was scared of the death slide but I went down it and now I'm not scared anymore and everyone was proud of me!

Finally, we went back to the car and drove off and saw a lot more things and had tea back home.

Reegan Parkes (7)
St Mark's VA Primary School, Worle

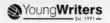

Dear Diary

Today, we went to a big zoo. I went with my friends. We took the car. On the way, we stopped at the petrol station for some food and fuel. I got a small drink and a sandwich. My friends got the same as me.

When we got there, we got a ticket. We got on the train to the zoo!

When we got off the train, we were at the big zoo! The first animal we saw was a zebra. The zebra was really stripy. The pattern was white and black. He had a friend. The next stop was the ice cream shop because it was really, really hot! I had a strawberry ice cream, it was awesome. Then I saw an owl, it was white with black dots.

At lunchtime, we had a picnic. I had pie. It was awesome. For pudding, I had a big cake. Then we went to see more animals. I saw a monkey and a rhino. The monkey was brown. The rhino was white and grey. After that, we went home. I had a nice time.

Isobel Owen (7)

St Mark's VA Primary School, Worle

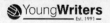

Dear Diary

Yesterday, I went to the funfair in the pink, big car really fast with Daddy, Mummy, Leah, Layla and Rupert. We went on the huge, big Ferris wheel. Then we went on the roller coaster. The sun was shining brightly. We went to the funfair because it was my birthday. We saw a huge, gold unicorn statue. Then we went to the big café and had our scrumptious lunch. We had a burger with tomatoes, cheese and my brother had cucumber.

After lunch, we played a game and I won a trophy. Then we got candyfloss and a chocolate smoothie. We had a treat.

We went to the unicorn shop and bought a unicorn teddy, a flip over top and a rainbow skirt and slime. We all got one. Then we went inside a red tent and we saw a magician. He got a rabbit out of his hat.

We got to keep it. We went to a clown juggling, then we got in the car and we went to sleep.

Lorelai Jimmieson (6)

St Mark's VA Primary School, Worle

Dear Diary

Today, I went to the beach to ride on a donkey. When we arrived, I picked a donkey called Scarlett. When I called her name, guess what happened? Scarlett turned into a unicorn!
Suddenly, I turned around and I saw a mermaid in the sea. I hopped on Scarlett's back and she ran to the end of the beach and back. Suddenly, she stopped in the middle of the beach. I got an ice cream and a chocolate milkshake. I got Scarlett some chocolate and we shared some pick 'n' mix. I gave Scarlett to Mum and Dad. I did some dancing and some swimming with the mermaid. Scarlett did some tricks. My favourite trick was the hand walk. I tried to do it. It took a long time until I got the hang of it.
After that, I hopped on Scarlett's back.

We went from one side of the beach to the other and back again. After that, I rode Scarlett home.

Payton Lillie Stacey (7)

St Mark's VA Primary School, Worle

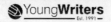
Dear Diary

Today, I went to the funfair with my mum and dad and my best friend Emily was coming with me. We went really fast in our black car. My mum packed us some lunch in a bag.

When we got there, me and Emily went on the helter-skelter and then we went on the spinning wheel, the sky got dark, but me and Emily kept playing games.

Suddenly, the sky got a bit darker, but we still kept playing games. We went on the merry-go-round, then we all did hook-a-duck.

We also went to the face paint station, then went off to have another go on the helter-skelter. There was a big queue so we had to wait forever, it felt like an hour, but finally, me and Emily got a go, but poor Mum and Dad were at the back of the queue.

This was the best bit, we got to go to the candyfloss stall! We saw Mum and Dad go down the helter-skelter.

Erin Robinson (7)
St Mark's VA Primary School, Worle

Dear Diary

Yesterday, I went to the park with Lorelai, Layla and Evalynn. It was magical because it was snowing! We played on the swings, slide and the zip wire. After that, we found a wand on the floor and I picked it up. I pointed it on the floor and the grass turned into an ice rink. We had glittery ice skates, so we started to skate. Then we found a secret tunnel. We went inside and a unicorn said, "Help me! Someone is trying to kill me."

"A dragon is trying to kill you," we said.

Then we made a net. After we made the net, we put it over the dragon and went back out of the tunnel. The sun was shining so the ice rink had started to melt and our ice skates came off.

After that, we all went home and had dinner. "The dinner is lovely," said Layla and Evalynn.

Leah Gordon (7)

St Mark's VA Primary School, Worle

Dear Diary

Yesterday, I went back in time to Dinosaur Land. I had a great time there. I saw a T-rex! It was scary, but at the same time, it was cute and tall. Meanwhile, I saw another dinosaur. I forgot what it was called but I liked it.

Later, I found a portal. It led me back to the normal world. I didn't go in it though. I had brought some snacks. They were delicious. I saw a tyrannosaurus rex. After lunch, it almost stepped on me! I was really scared. After that, I saw a brachiosaurus rex. I liked it. I hopped on his back so I could ride him. I named him Tall Dino.

I found the portal again. I didn't want to go in, so I made a dinosaur go in it. Everybody in the real world was scared. I found a portal, it led to zombies. I went in it. I wasn't scared.

Stephen Vowles (7)

St Mark's VA Primary School, Worle

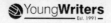

Dear Diary

A few months ago, I went to the cinema. I went with my dad. We went to Cineworld in my dad's van. After that, we went in. I had to go up the escalator, all the way to the top. Before we went to Cineworld, we visited Clip 'n' Climb.

At Clip 'n' Climb, there are giant climbing frames. The scariest one is the giant rainbow one.

Then we reached the cinema. We used the little machine to get a ticket to get in the cinema. We bought sweets, drinks and popcorn! I sat down on the chairs outside the cinema room. We scanned our ticket on the scanner outside the room. We went in the room. It had a big screen with lots of red lights. I was watching 'Avengers: Endgame'. The movie was really good and my sweets were really nice. I then went home.

Charlie Mortimer (7)

St Mark's VA Primary School, Worle

Dear Diary

Yesterday, I went to a funfair. I went on some rides in the morning. My favourite ride was the roller coaster. It was called Maximus and it was amazing.

At lunchtime, we had some hot dogs and I got a milkshake. For pudding, I had a waffle with bubble gum sauce and it was delicious. Just before the end of the day, we went on some more rides and after that, we went to go and buy some tickets for a circus that was there. It was busy and I got lost. To my shock, I saw some superheroes. I ran to them and I couldn't believe my eyes. I was talking to them and I told them everything. They said they could help me. I hopped onto one's back and flew up in the air. I saw my family and I jumped down to meet my mum. I told her what happened.

Max Fitzgibbon (6)
St Mark's VA Primary School, Worle

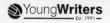

Dear Diary

In the holidays, I went to a funfair. It was amazing. I went with my gran, my dog, my cousins, my brothers, my sister, my mum and my dad. We walked for two hours to get there. Our legs were aching but it was very fun. I picked a duck up and it had a number 8. I went on a spinning ride. My mum and my cousin, Rianna, were with me. I was scared but then we got twisted, it was fine then. Gran had to go home because she had come to our caravan. Then we had to go, but it was really fun and we were still at the fair. We were waiting for my sister, Jessica. She was on a bouncing thing. It was fun for her, not me. I thought it wasn't fun because all you have to do is bounce.
Gran came round the next morning at 10:30 so I could go there again.

Lauren Barlow (7)
St Mark's VA Primary School, Worle

Dear Diary

On Monday, I went to the funfair with a good monster. We had to pay for a ticket to go to the funfair. When we got inside, there was a water park. We went in the pool. When we got out of the pool, we saw a secret tunnel. We went in the secret tunnel. When we got to the end of the tunnel, there was a secret room with all the stuff we like so we decided to play all the stuff. First, we played on all the tablets. Next, we played on all the Nintendo Switches. Then we had some of the delicious snacks. Next, we saw a sign saying: *Free Money. Come and Get Free Money!* We got so scared. We ate all the snacks, took all the money and ran, never to return.

Freddie Colman (7)

St Mark's VA Primary School, Worle

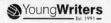

Dear Diary

Yesterday, I went to Harry Potter Land with my mum, dad and sister. The sun was shining. I got a Harry Potter toy. I also got an ice cream because it was so hot. I met Harry Potter. He was cool. He was fun.
I went on a ride with my dad and he screamed really loudly. Everyone stared at him and my mum laughed. I went into the gift shop and got a Harry Potter wand and a book and a teddy for my sister.
After the gift shop, we went on another ride with my dad. I met one of my friends who I saw in the gift shop. She bought a wand and a book like me. We went on a ride with her. She has a Harry Potter toy like me too.

Olivia Knott (7)
St Mark's VA Primary School, Worle

Dear Diary

I went to Spain. I went in the hot tub and it was hot! I turned the temperature to cool. The day after, I got back in the hot tub and listened to music and I danced with the jets on. It was bubbly.

Later that day, I got in the hot tub again but I had the lights on. It was cool. I had tea, it was pasta. It was so yummy. I could eat four buckets of pasta!

When I finished my food, I had chocolate cake. It was so yummy. I had a drink, it was apple juice.

When I got home, I played cards. I won!

The day after, I went to the circus and there was a man juggling with fire. It was amazing and scary.

Jacob Mikulla (7)
St Mark's VA Primary School, Worle

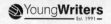
Dear Diary

Today, I went to space! I saw an alien. I
went with my family and superheroes. They
were a boy a girl. We had a swim because it
was so hot. We got a GoPro so we could
film underwater. We played 'who can guess
the song underwater'. No one guessed
mine. It was easy to guess Mollie-Sue's. It
was 'Kiki, Do You Love Me'.
We met an astronaut. He said, "Yo!" It
means hello in astronaut language. After
that, we built sandcastles and then we went
home to the funfair with my best friend,
Lauren. I got a toy from the claw machine. I
got a tub of money.

Lola Jessie Dyer (7)
St Mark's VA Primary School, Worle

Dear Diary

On Friday afternoon, after school, I went to Paul's campsite with my mum and her two friends. After they set up the tent and unpacked everything, I went to ride on my scooter around the shop up the hill and the down the hill.

The next day, I had a pain au chocolat for breakfast. After that, I went to ride on my scooter. When I went back to the tent, I went on my tablet and built a tree house. Next, I added someone to play with me and they helped me build the tree house. After that, they built a house next door to me and I made a secret trail to their house.

Jaiden Moore (7)
St Mark's VA Primary School, Worle

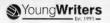
Dear Diary

I went horse riding. I went with my best friend and my family. I saw a unicorn. I started riding it. I saw a shop, so we got off our horses and went into the shop. I got some chocolate and then went home.

My best friend was near and we played our favourite horse game. Then me and my friend went out to the shop and I got some more chocolate. We went to the lake, the unicorn was splashing in the lake.

In the morning, I woke up and my friend was eating lunch. Then after lunch, we went out. My horse was eating hay. We tacked up the horse and went on a ride.

Jessica Ambrose (7)
St Mark's VA Primary School, Worle

Dear Diary

On Sunday, I went to the zoo with a unicorn, We went in a silver, shiny car. When we got there, we had to get a ticket, so people knew we had paid. Then we got a map to show us where we were going. First, we saw the zebras. They were black and white. They also had stripes and their bodies had lots of stripes on them.

Next, we saw the lions. They were very loud and had very long tails. They had very fluffy manes and fur.

Finally, we saw the giraffes. They had very long legs and very, very long necks. They were very big and a lot bigger than me.

May Bailey (7)
St Mark's VA Primary School, Worle

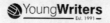

Dear Diary

Yesterday, I went to Poole. When we got there, we went to the hotel. It was a special day because we were going to Monkey World! We drove a long way and saw lots of trees. First, we bought a ticket and then we went in. It was amazing! I loved the howler monkeys best. I love it because they made funny noises. Then we went to the cafe. Next, we went to the playground. I liked adventure ropes the best. Then we went to the gift shop. I got a fluffy gibbon. I had so much fun. I would like to go back to Poole again.

Jessica Cunningham (7)
St Mark's VA Primary School, Worle

Dear Diary

I went to the mall. First, I went to F Hinds with my sister Ellie, my cousin Darcy, Daddy and Mummy. At F Hinds, I got a pretty ring. Then we got back in the car and went to Pizza Hut. Mummy had a pineapple pizza, I had a pepperoni pizza, Darcy had a cheese pizza, Daddy had a pepperoni pizza and Ellie had a chicken pizza. For pudding, we had ice cream.

We got back in the car and went to the beach. It got dark so we went to Darcy's house and she went to bed. Then we went home too and went to bed.

Bella Elizabeth Cawley (7)

St Mark's VA Primary School, Worle

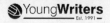
Dear Diary

Today, we went in the car and we had my grandma's dog. His name is Billy. We reached the park. We got to the lovely green fields. Billy found a ball, but the lady wanted it back. It was really hard to get back because he had it in his mouth and he wouldn't let go of it. It was really funny to see my mum try and get it off him. I told my mum to call his name and everyone then started to call his name, even the lady. It was really funny because people kept on saying his name. It made my head spin.

Carly McDermott (7)
St Mark's VA Primary School, Worle

Dear Diary

I was on holiday at a swimming pool. We had the most fun in the whole entire world! I had the best day ever because I was diving, star jumping and pencil jumping into the pool. I was the best one there. Chloe, my swimming teacher, was watching us. I was having the best time and Isa was too. Mummy was getting wet glasses and it was funny! I loved diving into the pool! Isa had fun as well. I also had fun in there and it was so fun. Mummy bought a packet of crisps and Isa had a packet of star chocolates.

Connie Harvey-Comer (7)
St Mark's VA Primary School, Worle

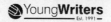

Dear Diary

On Tuesday, I went to the park with a shimmering mermaid and a glamorous unicorn.

At the park, we had a bar of chocolate and it was yummy. After that, we made some gooey slime. It was multicoloured with some swirls. Next, we did some colourful art and then we did some awesome gymnastics. Afterwards, we had a party and it was fantastic.

We later went swimming in the garden, then had a little disco. After lunch, we went horse riding and a fairy came to ride with us.

What an amazing day!

Layla Enver (7)

St Mark's VA Primary School, Worle

Dear Diary

One day, I joined a football team and I saw lots of people watching. They were happy and cheering. I was happy too. I like football now because I'm used to it. It's really fun! Football matches are fun. My teammates are funny! It's great and my teammates are good.
One day, I crossed one in. It was a great goal! It was amazing! I love my team, they are the best team I have ever played for! I have three man of the match trophies. I was excited and it was the best time of my life.

Ellis D'Arcy
St Mark's VA Primary School, Worle

Dear Diary

At the zoo, I went with my mum and dad. It took three hours to get there.
When I got there, I saw a tiger. It was scary because it was spiky! It was orange. We went to see the giraffe. It had lots of spots and a long neck.
We had a cheeseburger and a strawberry milkshake for lunch. We had fun at the zoo. Zoos are my favourite thing and very fun. When I got back, I had a cup of tea and relaxed and watched 'Alvin and the Chipmunks' on TV. Then I went to bed.

Leon Neate (6)
St Mark's VA Primary School, Worle

Dear Diary

I went to the park with my best friend. We had lunch and a drink. After that, we made slime. We then went to the shop and I got a kitten. My best friend, Lola, got a sheep. We then took Lola home and I went home too. Next, I played a game on my Xbox.

The next day, I went to a party and had sweets and played football. Next, I went on a treasure hunt but my mum couldn't find the treasure map.

The next day, I went outside and I saw a butterfly and a dragonfly.

Lillie-Rose Biss (7)

St Mark's VA Primary School, Worle

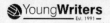

Dear Diary

Yesterday, I went to the park. I went with my family.

When we got there, we played football. I won by ten points. Then we went on the swing and it was fun. The slide was better than the swing though, but most of all, my favourite was the zip line.

After that, it was evening. I had a big burger, chips and a milkshake. It was the best ever. I was full up. Then I went on the seesaw. It wasn't the best of them. It was the best day ever. Then we went home.

James Morrissey (7)
St Mark's VA Primary School, Worle

Dear Diary

In the summer, I went to the park and it was a sunny day. I went with my nanny and Toby. Toby's my nanny's dog. I was sick that day. I was poorly on Monday and Tuesday. I went to Disney and I saw Spider-Man. At Disneyland Paris, I saw Cinderella and Snow White. I also saw Belle at Disneyland. I had a smoothie and it was very cold but it was yummy. I made a fairy. I planted some basil seeds and I did my Brownie promise at Brownies.

Rosie Seckham (7)
St Mark's VA Primary School, Worle

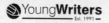

Dear Diary

One Wednesday, I played a match with Dexter, Harry, Cieran and David. I scored nine goals. It was boiling hot and we won 12-0. We were playing for Priory Pumas. It was easy. Me and Dexter did a one-two, then I put it away into the bottom corner. Then every couple of minutes, I scored. Then George scored with two nutmegs into the bottom corner. It was so much fun.
I had chicken curry for tea. Dexter let me have some of his Oreos.

Logan Hughes (7)
St Mark's VA Primary School, Worle

Dear Diary

Yesterday, I went to cinema to watch 'Secret Life of Pets 2'. It was funny. Dad and Mum and me laughed.

After that, we drove back home in our white car.

At lunchtime, we ate a jam sandwich and an apple, a Cheestring and some crisps and a banana. After lunch, we went on the beach. On the beach, we had an ice cream. Me and Dad played football on the beach.

Harry Hucker (7)

St Mark's VA Primary School, Worle

Dear Diary

I went to Hawaii's beach with my friend. We went scuba diving with an underwater metal detector.
After a while, we saw an amazing thing under the water. It was a £100 ring and a tub of money.
The next day, me and my dad went to the beach and we found a bomb with the metal detector!
We went back to the hotel and packed up and went home.

Ashton Robinson (7)
St Mark's VA Primary School, Worle

Dear Diary

I went to the fair. There were lots of rides, but there were only two rides open. Blake, my brother, went on both of the rides. I only went on one ride, but I cried because it was going too fast.

I got there in a van, it had six seats! I sat at the back with my sister, Courtney. I loved it there. I went to bed at 9pm. I normally go to bed at 7pm.

Darci Garside (7)
St Mark's VA Primary School, Worle

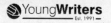

Dear Diary

I went to space with a monster and Erin. We got there in a car, but it was a magic car. It was scary on the trip and long.
We got there and were hungry so we had some slime and chocolate and sweets and a drink because I was really thirsty. It was cool and cold and dark and scary and really quiet. We could jump really high!

Oliver James Walton (7)
St Mark's VA Primary School, Worle

Dear Diary

One day, I went to the funfair. There was also beautiful green grass and some beautiful trees and flowers. It was a long way to Bristol. It was really fun! We saw bumper cars, Toon Town, inflatable ball slides. There was also a metal slide. It was really fast. We also watched a magic show while we were having lunch.

Ciaran Rees (7)
St Mark's VA Primary School, Worle

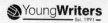
Dear Diary

On Saturday, I went to Brean Splash. I liked the Nemo slide. I liked the yellow slide. My best part was the big pool. I don't like going outside because of the cold and the wind. I like Brean Splash because of the slides and the water guns. I liked the Death Chomper. Outside there are more slides.

Jax Ager (6)
St Mark's VA Primary School, Worle

Dear Diary

Yesterday, me and my brother were playing with Lego. We built a construction site. I built little pieces and my brother built big pieces.
When it is finished, I think it will look really good. Next, we are going to build a house and a car.

Harrison Roberts (7)
St Mark's VA Primary School, Worle

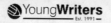
Dear Diary

Yesterday, my mum wouldn't let me go to Brean Splash. Maybe if I get a magic key to find a magic door, it might take me into a portal. The first thing I might do is go on the diving boards with my family.

Rory Bishop (7)
St Mark's VA Primary School, Worle

Dear Diary

Yesterday, I did a tabletop sale. I did it with one of my BFFs and she's called Amaya and my mummy helped us.

When people started walking around, we got so excited and at one point there were twenty people wanting to buy something at our stall. It was funny when people were walking around and we were just setting up. It was so tiring when we raced back and forwards across the street.

After that, we went to Archie's house and watched him play on his television. When he finished that game, we went to Ethan's house, they were selling sweets, me and Amaya got a bag each. Then we raced back to my house. Then it started to rain, so me and Amaya went into the house. We started to play babies, then Amaya had to go home. I was so tired, I went to sleep. Zzz.

Scarlett (7)
Sunninghill Preparatory School, South Walks

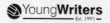

Dear Diary

On Saturday morning, I woke up a little later than usual. It was 8:30am by the time I came downstairs. The first thing I did was give my guinea pig Camilla Pumpkin a big cuddle. Camilla loves cucumber so I gave her that for breakfast. She is such a funny fatty bottom and can be quite a stroppy knickers at times but I love her very much. After breakfast, my brothers Cameron, Taylor and Charlie, Mummy and Daddy and I took our dogs Nookie and Digby for a walk at Moreton. Nookie only likes to walk if we stop for cream teas. Usually, Nookie plods along, but when there is a promise of a cake, she runs like an Olympic athlete.
In the afternoon, Mummy, Daddy, Charlie and I went to a summer fayre. We learnt some circus skills and Mummy rode a bull! I had my face painted like a beautiful mermaid.

We had a very busy day and I was ready for bed by 7pm. Merlin my cat came in for a cuddle as I went to sleep.

Tabitha Margarette May Buchan-Moore (7)

Sunninghill Preparatory School, South Walks

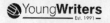
Dear Diary

On holiday, we sailed the Greek islands. Every morning, Daddy would work out the route for the day and I'd play with Freddie and Max on the beach.

One morning, we tried to get the anchor up, but it was trapped under a rock, so Daddy had to dive down with some other men to move it. Some people pulled the anchor and some pushed the rock and at last, we were free! We sailed away to the next island and I saw a big turtle on the way. Freddie and I sat on the front of the yacht and got sprayed by the waves. It was lovely because we were so hot and the water made us feel cool.

In the evening, we moored at the harbour and walked along the quay to get an ice cream and play on the beach before dinner. I had a yummy strawberry ice cream.

Leo Hemingway (7)
Sunninghill Preparatory School, South Walks

Dear Diary

Yesterday, I went to the beach and canoed to our boat.

When we got there, I dived down to the bottom and took up the anchor. Daddy said that I could dive, which was really exciting. I kneeled up and we went so fast that I nearly fell over, it was amazing.

We used the map to find the best fishing spot, which was by an old shipwreck. My rod got tangled up with fins, but my rod caught a mackerel and Daddy helped untangle it.

After that, Theo and I got in the canoe and we were towed behind the boat. The canoe was bending because we were going so fast and the water was splashing everywhere. Theo fell off three times, but I didn't because I was the king of the canoe. We laughed so much, it was the best day ever!

Natty Savva (7)

Sunninghill Preparatory School, South Walks

Dear Diary

Yesterday, I went to Granny and Grandpa's and I went to a big party. I played, had ice cream and played football. There was a lot of tackling and there was music, which I listened to quite a lot. I went home and watched telly and then I went to bed.

This morning, I played and this evening, Mum and Dad came back from London with lots of presents for me. Clothes and Lego! I had a big forage around in the bags and found camouflage shorts and a Lego set. I felt very pleased and I was very excited and happy.

I can't wait to make the Lego set after school tomorrow and join it to my monster truck from 'Lego Movie 2'. They are both from 'Lego Movie 2', in case you didn't know!

Albi Bryant (7)
Sunninghill Preparatory School, South Walks

Dear Diary

Once, I had a dream. It was about a pig and a dog. The pig was very pink. It had a curly tail. The dog had a pink tutu.

Once, they went into town, they went on a bouncy castle and *pop!* The pig went *oink* when they fell off! So they went home.

The next day, they went to the farm and went in some mud. The pig went *oink* and the dog went *woof, bark, bark, woof.* Then they went home again! Then I woke up and thought, *what's going on?* Never mind, I think it was just a dream. Tonight, I hope I dream about going to the park and space.

Georgiana Hume (7)

Sunninghill Preparatory School, South Walks

Dear Diary

Today, I was feeling nervous, excited, scared and happy. I had yummy pancakes for breakfast to get my energy up. It took us forty-five minutes to get to the tennis club. First, we had two practice matches against our own team and then it started raining super heavily. It rained so horrendously that we had to go to West Hants Tennis Club for the matches.

Then the match got serious. We played hard against West Hants, our team won third place and I won three matches. We all received certificates and we all went home happy.

Ren Ren Zhou (6)
Sunninghill Preparatory School, South Walks

Dear Diary

Today, I went to the zoo with my family. We saw lots of animals, my favourite was the kangaroo because we got to feed it and it was so soft. Then we had lunch, I had a burger and chips, for my drink I had water with ice cubes. After that, we went to the playground, me and Maggie raced on the ninja course that was at the park. We went back to the kangaroo and fed it again, it felt amazing. We walked to the bus stop, my legs were so tired I had a rest and finally, the bus came. We went home and had dinner, I had curry.

Millie Amy Hooper-Greenhill (7)
Sunninghill Preparatory School, South Walks

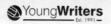
Dear Diary

I have had the craziest day of my life. When I woke up, I was in a room full of dragon heads hanging from the ceiling, swords on the walls and a suit of armour where my dressing gown should be! When I went downstairs, I was so shocked I almost screamed. I saw a person carving meat, piping hot soup and a boar's head on the table. I heard a clanking noise and went to see what it was. There was a blacksmith making armour, swords and shields. "Hope you have a good time fighting the dragon today."

"Erm, okay," I said and went to test them out. They were so tough that I thought, *wow, they are indestructible!* He explained that metal was forged from the teeth of a giant monster that my brother Sir Theo collected. I tried to look cool but in my mind, I was thinking, *what on earth is going on?*

As I was wandering back to eat more breakfast, the trumpets sounded and my mum and dad appeared in the most ridiculous clothes cheering, "Good luck, brave son."

So off I rode to Mount Dragon. The dragon was sleeping, it was gobsmackingly ginormous. It opened one eye and breathed out fire, but I dodged.

After hours of fighting, I leapt onto its back and chopped off its head in one swoop.

"Phew!" I said and in the blink of an eye, I was home.

Charlie Janisch (7)

Umberleigh Primary School, Umberleigh

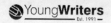

Dear Diary

You won't believe it but I have just been on the most exciting adventure in the world... I went to the funfair and I saw a candyfloss stall so I bought some and sat on a bench and ate it.

Next, I went on the helter-skelter and it was very fast. When I was on it, I saw a bouncy castle and I went on it and jumped as high as the sky. When I jumped off it, I saw a Slush Puppie stand and I just had to get one. It was strawberry and raspberry flavour.

When I eventually finished my Slush Puppie, I saw a lucky dip, so I got one. When I opened it, there was a rocket, and when I opened the rocket, it was full of fairy dust and there was a tiny fairy. She told me to sprinkle some fairy dust on my hair, so I did and I turned into a fairy. Me and the other fairy flew home.

I sprinkled some more fairy dust on me and I turned back into a human and I put the other fairy into the rocket and went to bed.

Vhari Findlay-Wilson (7)

Umberleigh Primary School, Umberleigh

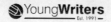

Dear Diary

Once upon a time, there was a princess named Ruby. She went to her dad's mine with him, where there was a treasure map. There were X marks the spot. When they got to the middle, they saw a bat prince that loved Ruby. They got to a T-junction... they went right and then went on.

Suddenly, a big dragon jumped out at Ruby, but she was not scared because it was a dragonlet. They carried on and on until they met a pack of wolves. Ruby's dad swung his sword side to side and they ran away home. Then a big, big bad wolf came and there was a fight. Ruby and her dad carried on and they saw something sparkling in the moonlight. There was the treasure! The ruby-red diamond! Her dad gently took the ruby-red diamond. Ruby said, "That was the best adventure!"

Ruby Mae Charlemagne (6)
Umberleigh Primary School, Umberleigh

Dear Diary

On Wednesday, Cece and I met up with Ruby and Andrew. Cece is my sister, Ruby is my best friend and Andrew is a purple alien. One day, we went to Puppy Land. We saw hundreds and hundreds of puppies. We soon realised that we weren't standing and were being carried by puppies! But we didn't know where we were going. We realised we were going to the puppy palace. We had been brought to the puppy king. The puppy king said to us, "A little puppy ran away." We went to search for the little puppy. Andrew scanned the land.
At last, we found the cheeky puppy and brought it to the king.

Lily Capaldi (5)
Umberleigh Primary School, Umberleigh

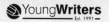
Dear Diary

I went to the zoo. I saw zebras and a python snake. My favourite was the flamingos. I had a blueberry ice cream.

Emilia Locke (5)

Umberleigh Primary School, Umberleigh

Dear Diary

Yesterday, I found a portal leading to lands of magical creatures on the London Underground. I walked through. As you could all imagine, I was surprised. Especially when I saw dragons and griffins flying around me, a griffin is half lion and half eagle but orange. I walked further to see free theme park rides. There were spiders, cockroaches, dragons, unicorns and all sorts of bugs and mythical creatures. I found a dragon, the man next to me said it wanted to fly, I said I could fly it. The man's name was Mark and the dragon was Harry. I hopped onto Harry and realised all the other dragons had launched up into the air as well.

After the amazing ride, I was sucked back through the portal, back to the London Underground. That was the most amazing day of my life (so far).

Oliver Lewis (7)

Whiteparish All Saints Primary School, Whiteparish

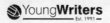

Dear Diary

On Friday, I went to a friend's house, we saw a huge grey elephant appear. I ran upstairs and saw a monkey. It screeched into the kitchen and glared at the banana and pinched it. A chicken transported into a bowl and squirted egg out, it felt magical. I stretched and grabbed my drink where a large, confused goldfish blew lots of small bubbles and tried to swim away.

Ten minutes later, I thought of an amazing plan. I tiptoed to the white feathery chicken and grabbed the bowl, it was filled with fresh eggs. I smacked the chicken and it flew away. Suddenly, I quickly had super strength, I darted and nudged the grey elephant, it almost knocked the door down. Suddenly, a splash came from upstairs, I bolted to my room and the fish grew. The cup smashed onto the floor. I grabbed the wet, squelchy fish and put it in a blue, spotty cup, then I sprinted to the small, blue

lake. I put the fish in and went back to the house.
The monkey! I thought. I heard a crash. "Oh no!" It knocked a bedside light down. "There's going to be trouble..."

Seren Elder (7)
Whiteparish All Saints Primary School, Whiteparish

Dear Diary

Today, I shrank down to the size of a Barbie doll and went on an adventure around my garden. First, I hiked up my climbing frame and when I reached the top, I could see for miles! I bravely whooshed back down to the ground on the high, green, wavy slide at fifty miles an hour. I landed in a flower bed and when I looked up, I saw my red windmill towering above me, spinning in the breeze. It was so windy it nearly blew me away! Just then, I heard a plodding sound. Charlie, my pet tortoise, came to rescue me. I climbed upon his high back and took a ride to the pear tree, where I took a big bite from a giant pear. It was so juicy. Then I heard lots of laughing. My dolls were having a pool party in my princess paddling pool! I climbed in and joined them. We had races on the backs of rubber ducks. I started to feel very tired, my eyes were closing, but suddenly, I began to grow up and up until I was my size again. My mum came out and asked me why I was asleep in the pool!

Ella Davidson (6)
Whiteparish All Saints Primary School, Whiteparish

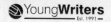

Dear Diary

On Monday, at Peach Lane Fairy School, I learnt a tidy bedroom spell. This afternoon I tried it, but it went seriously wrong. My whole bedroom turned into a fish tank. Now I can't sleep in my bed, it's soaking!
On Tuesday, I learnt another spell, it was a tidy garden spell. When I got home, I did it and I did it wrong again. This time, the garden turned into a tank.
On Wednesday, we learnt how to make a trampoline spell. After school, I tried it and it made a wine bottle.
On Thursday, we all learnt to make clothes. When I got home, I tried it. It went dreadfully wrong, everything turned into draws.
Finally, it came to Friday and we learnt to tidy our whole house. It was disastrous, our house exploded!

Lottie Shutler (7)
Whiteparish All Saints Primary School, Whiteparish

Dear Diary

On Saturday, we went to see Matilda at the theatre, it was incredible how they were acting. Miss Trunchbull was very funny because she said, "There is a newt in my knickers." One boy ate a whole cake and did not stop eating. I do not know how they do it. Matilda is a good place to go to. My favourite bit was when the children sang 'When I Grow Up'. Matilda loves to read books from the library but this made her Mummy and Daddy cross. Matilda makes friends with Lavender. Miss Honey is very kind to Matilda and asks her to go and live with her. Matilda is now happy.
I loved Matilda and we also had sweets and ice cream at the theatre.

Sophie Martin (6)
Whiteparish All Saints Primary School, Whiteparish

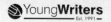

Dear Diary

On Saturday 1st June, I started football training at a new football club. I didn't know anyone, I was really brave and joined straight in and made lots of new friends. I scored one goal.

On Saturday 22nd June, I went football training again. It was nice to see all my friends again. We did a bit of training, then we played a match. I didn't score any goals on this day.

On Saturday 29th June, I went to football training. First, we did some training and then we played a match, I scored a hat-trick, that's three goals, and I got man of the match. I was given a trophy to take home. I was so happy.

Alfie Greig Hatch (7)
Whiteparish All Saints Primary School, Whiteparish

Dear Diary

At the weekend, we went to a train station in Yorkshire. Daddy got tickets for the train so we could ride all day on the train. I saw a beautiful green countryside with flowers and animals. I got hungry on the train so Daddy gave me a KitKat biscuit.
At lunchtime, we had a picnic by the park. I liked the slide and the tunnel because they were fun. It was a lovely day.

Jack Bryant (6)
Whiteparish All Saints Primary School, Whiteparish

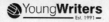

Dear Diary

One day, I met a unicorn. Her name was Lilly. Then I flew to her house.
When I arrived there, there were more unicorns having a party. They played tag. Then it was bedtime, so the unicorn took me home to bed.

Rosie Leach (5)
Whiteparish All Saints Primary School, Whiteparish

Dear Diary

On Saturday, I went to Smyths toy store. I went with my mum, dad and my sister. I bought a Yellies, a Harry Scoots spider and a Fingerling whale. I also looked at the Toy Story 4 things. I showed Mum all the Toy Story 4 things that I would like. My favourites are Bo-Peep, Bullseye, Forky, Bunny and Ducky. I am now going to save up my pocket money to buy the Bunny and Ducky teddies.

Jessica Rose Vicary (7)

Whitleigh Community Primary School, Whitleigh

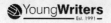

Dear Diary

On Saturday, I went to the zoo with my family. I met a new friend. We saw a tiger. I had a great time.
I had a sleepover at my nanny's. I watched a movie. I woke up and had pancakes and went on a bike ride.

Emmie Louise Thomas (7)
Whitleigh Community Primary School, Whitleigh

Dear Diary

Today, I went to the Co-op and got Dunkers and pizza. After, I went to Farmfoods. In the store, I got ice cream and another ice cream for my sister and then went home. After that, I went to sleep.

Winner Bazinga (6)
Whitleigh Community Primary School, Whitleigh

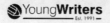

Dear Diary

During the holidays, I went to Derby with my family. In Derby, we watched football at the stadium. After that, we went for lunch. I had hot dogs and ice cream. We also played at the park.

Dexter Robertson (7)
Whitleigh Community Primary School, Whitleigh

Dear Diary

On Sunday, I went to the field with my grandad. We played football. We went back home to play Star Wars toys with everyone.

Jayden Pean (7)
Whitleigh Community Primary School, Whitleigh

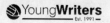
Dear Diary

I made cupcakes at home. I played Pokémon. I ate my lunch. I read my book. I played with my baby brother.

Jacob Ackland (6)
Whitleigh Community Primary School, Whitleigh